America's Rural Yesterday

Volume I: Fieldwork

Publisher's Cataloging-in-Publication
(Provided by Quality Books, Inc.)

America's Rural Yesterday. Volume 1, Fieldwork / featuring
  the photography of J.C. Allen & Son ; edited by Joe
  Mischka.
     p. cm.
     Includes bibliographical references and index.
     LCCN 2012953873
     ISBN 9781882199068

     1. Agriculture--United States--History--Pictorial
works. 2. Family farms--United States--History--
Pictorial works.   I. Mischka, Joe. II. J.C. Allen &
Son.

S520.A44 2012   630'.973
                           QBI12-600225

Contents

Introduction

One of the goals of our magazine, *Rural Heritage*, is to promote the small, diversified family farm — a small acreage with chickens, pigs, dairy and beef cows; corn, beans, oats, spelt and other field crops; large vegetable gardens producing bushels of beans, beets, cabbage, carrots, tomatoes and turnips; and a farmyard and house where all these things are harvested, preserved and enjoyed by multi-generational families working together.

This idyllic setting was the norm in the early part of the 20th Century in midwestern America. Farm sizes were limited by the type of power being used in the fields: horses, mules, oxen or early model tractors. Large families were useful — as much of the work was done by hand, and many hands made the work go more quickly.

At the same time, change was coming. Agriculture was beginning to benefit as farm equipment and supply companies began taking a more scientific approach to the profession of farming. Universities began developing larger agriculture programs, and seed and fertilizer companies competed for this developing market as new products were developed. For the first time, farming was treated as a *real* profession. Technological developments in soil and livestock sciences began making real impacts on the yields and bottom line on American farms.

These years, from roughly 1920 to 1945, were what I consider the heyday of American family farming. The men, women and children who worked the fields, tended the stock, and put up the crops would be long forgotten were it not for a few writers such as Ben Logan, Jerry Apps, Bob Artley, Roger Welsch, Michael Perry and others. A handful of photographers also helped preserve the images of the period, making it their mission to document the everyday life of rural families at work.

J.C. Allen and Sons, Inc., were arguably the best at this work. Centered in Lafayette, Ind., these photographers scoured the Midwest for farming photos. Tens of thousands of these prints are archived in the collection of J.C. Allen's grandson and photographer, John O. Allen. With John's help, we have collected some of the best of these photos to create a three-volume set. This book, the first in that series, features photographs of fieldwork: plowing, tillage, planting, cultivating, harvesting and fertilizer-spreading using horses, mules, oxen and an occasional tractor. The second book will cover the work performed in the farmyard: threshing, ensilaging, hay mow loading, sorghum pressing, butchering, making apple butter, and much more. Finally, the third book will focus on life in the kitchen, living room, school, dining room, town market and hardware store, and country road. Combined, we believe these three volumes provide a comprehensive picture of life in the early 1920s to the 1940s in rural America. It is a tribute to the people who took pride in operating the family farm and are responsible for so many of the best values and traditions we hold dear today.

— Joe Mischka

A rural Indiana family takes the team to town.

Above. Two rotary hoes on the farm of W.S. Corsa, White Hall, Ill.

Right. Four mules pull a spike tooth harrow.

America's Rural Yesterday

Chapter 1: Tillage

Plowing.
Twelve horses on
a 3-bottom sulky
plow.

Discing. An early Mogul tractor pulls a pair of discs heavily anchored with rocks and logs in 1916.

Raking Corn Stalks. A very early type of dump rake is used to rake corn stalks in the mid 1910s.

Knocking Down Corn Stalks. A long pole pulled between two teams helps knock down corn stalks left behind after harvest.

Plowing. A team of yoked oxen provides the power to this walking plow. The team is controlled by lines running to the yoke and then to the steers' horns.

Mixed Power. An Allis-Chalmers tractor discs and harrows to cover oats broadcast by a team of horses near Otterbein, Ind., in 1932. Note how the driver of the team has the lines looped over one arm.

||||||||||||||||||||||||||||||||||||||||||||||||||||||||||||

Mules. Virgil Weaver, West Point, Ind., harrows with a hitch of white mules.

||||||||||||||||||||||||||||||||||||||||||||||||||||||||||||

Another. Virgil Weaver's hitch of mules continues its work harrowing his field. Virgil drives the center team. The two outside mules are bridled with straps running to the trace keepers of the mule beside them.

Harrowing. Four mules pull a spike-tooth harrow that is pulling a two-wheeled cart behind it to allow the driver a chance to ride instead of walk.

Fast Plowing. Two sets of five-horse teams on one-bottom sulkies covered a lot of ground before needing a rest.

Above and Right. Three well-matched Percheron work horses pull a sulky plow.

Plowing with oxen.
The man driving the very nice team of oxen appears to be dressed for some kind of special event, and the plow is a very nice reproduction of a primitive plow.

Above. A farmer and his horses cultivate sudan grass on this Plains, Kan., farm in 1932.

Above. Five Percherons and one mule disc and harrow at the Charles Rutan farm near Frankfort, Ind.

Right. Six Percherons plowing in 1938.

Above. Father, son, daughter and dog pose on a new Allis-Chalmers Model W tractor pulling a disc in corn stubble.

Right. Eight beautiful mules with two sulky plows create perfectly straight furrows on the Charles Kelly Ranch near Monon, Ind.

||||||||||||||||||||||||||||||||||||||||||||||||||||||||||||||||||||||||||

Above. Preparing seed bed with purebred Percherons on the farm of General Harry C. Tresder of Allentown, Penn.

||||||||||||||||||||||||||||||||||||||||||||||||||||||||||||||||||||||||||

Right. A team of Percherons pull a stalled tractor put to a sulky plow.

Above and Right. Four Percherons plowing corn stubble.

Above and Right. In the foreground, eighteen Percherons pull discs and harrows. In the background, two teams of Percherons plant corn on the Penny-Givinn farm near Noblesville, Ind.

||||||||||||||||||||||||||||||||||||||||||||||||||||||||||||||||||||||||||||||||||

Above. A hitch of six mules and another of six horses disc on the farm of Charles McHarry in Attica, Ind.

Right. The same hitches are later combined to pull a large drag.

Plowing. Six Percherons on a two-bottom plow.

Dragging. A team of horses pull a drag at the home of Edgar M. Cheever near Brooksburg, Ind. A small boy rides the left-hand horse while chickens peck for insects in the soil disturbed by the drag.

Rolling. A team of mules in Montgomery, Ala., pull a roller on the farm of L.C. Young and Son.

America's Rural Yesterday

Chapter 2: Planting

Left. Planting corn with a team of mules and rope row markers.

Nine mules and a tractor, above. Preparing the seed bed and planting corn on the W.A. Wilkey Co. farm near Sullivan, Ind.

Harvest & Plant. In one pass, this Tippecanoe County, Ind., farmer cuts his soybeans and puts in winter wheat.

Drilling Grain. After the corn is shocked, a cover crop is drilled into the field.

Drilling grain. These four attractive horses are probably crossbreds, with plenty of Percheron. Notice the horse in the paddock in the background—perhaps a purebred Percheron stallion designed to add more draft to the breeding program.

Drilling oats, above. Drilling oats with four mules.

Planting beans. Two young lads are dropping beans for planting. The younger fellow, at right, is barefoot.

A long row to go. Four mules are drilling oats at the Carl Lee Bros. farm, England, Ark.

Above and Right. Using a drill to sow sweet clover and spread lime in wheat on the farm of William Vanderkeed, Lafayette, Ind.

Drilling wheat. A farmer drills wheat in a field from which a corn crop has been cut for silage at the Purdue Experimental Livestock farm, Lafayette, Ind.

Planting corn. A couple of powerful sorrel Belgians provide the power in this corn planting scene. Notice the row marker rope barely visible.

Planting corn. This time with Percherons.

More corn planting. Marvin Wise plants corn on his Delphi, Ind., farm.

Drilling grain.

Sweet Potatoes. Setting out sweet potato plants in a young apple orchard on the farm of N.Y. Yates, in Decker, Ind.

Left and Above. More grain drilling.

Cultivating and Fertilizing a field of tomato plants.

Tobacco. Applying fertilizer for tobacco on the farm of M. Wikles and Sons, Meigs, Ga.

Above. Another corn planting scene in rural Indiana.

Right. Drilling oats in cotton stalks on the farm of J.C. Guard, near Charlotte, N.C.

Above and Right. Filling the fertilizer hopper and then planting corn in a dusty field.

Double Drilling. Three tractors, two discs and two grain drills make quick work of getting in the crop.

America's Rural Yesterday
Chapter 3: Cultivating

||||||||||||||||||||||||||||||||||||||||||||||||||||||||||||||||||||||||||||

Cotton, above. Cultivating cotton on the Barlow-Roberts Plantation near Sherman, Texas.

||||||||||||||||||||||||||||||||||||||||||||||||||||||||||||||||||||||||||||

Dust Mulch. A single horse pulls a small sled that creates a mulch of fine dirt to cover emerging weeds.

Gardening, left. The farm garden and house of Merle Conract near West Point, Ind., who uses a Planet Jr wheeled-cultivator.

Mississipi, above. Cultivating cotton with two teams of handsome mules.

Hot work. Farm hands hoe cotton on the Delaney Bros. plantation near Clarksdale, Miss., in 1932.

Black and white teams. Cultivating cotton near Honey Grove, Texas.

Riding in Style. This farmer weeds his row crops in the shade.

Potatoes. A team of Belgians pulls a cultivator through a field of potatoes.

Plowing. Cultivating corn with three Percheron mares at the George Dix Farm, Deleware, Ohio.

Young corn. Cultivating young corn on the farm of C.E. James, Mansfield, Ill.

Percherons. Four Percherons cultivate corn at the E. Humbert Farm near Corning, Iowa, in 1939.

Young Men. A large farm garden is kept weed-free by a couple of hard working boys.

Cultivating Tobacco. Plowing between the tobacco rows on the farm of George Keller near Lexington, Ky.

Young corn. Discing between rows of orange trees at C.A. Zimmerman's farm in Anaheim, Calif., with a 1932 Case model CO.

Cultivating Corn. Mary and Martha Brown of Tippecanoe County, Ind., cultivate high corn with a team of horses and a team of mules, all muzzled.

America's Rural Yesterday

Chapter 4: Harvesting

Right and Opposite. An Indiana man uses a scythe and cradle to harvest and shock wheat.

Above. A team of black mules pull a homemade wagon slung low to allow easy loading and unloading of baled hay or straw.

Loaded. A hayrack is nearly fully-stacked with forage and pulled by two mules fitted with fly nets.

||||||||||||||||||||||||||||||||||||||||||||||||||||||||||||||||||||||||||||||||||||||||

Left. Corn shucking with horses and mules.

Above. Mules use bull rakes to bring straw to the stationary baler seen in the upper left of the photo.

Bringing it Home. A pair of white mules pull a wagon loaded with freshly-shucked corn.

Above. Harvesting potatoes on the farm of John Workman near Lafayette, Ind.

Sugaring. Collecting maple sap in Indiana.

Salad Days. A farmer harvests his beautiful batch of leaf lettuce.

Truck Farming. A couple pick and load large heads of cabbage.

All ears, above. Workers pick up ears of corn from a field of shocked corn on the Floyd Johnson farm, Frankfort, Ind.

Harvesting carrots, right. A small wooden wheelbarrow awaits a fresh bunch of carrots.

||||||||||||||||||||||||||||||||||||||||||||||||||||||||||||||||||||||||||||||||||||||||||||||||

Left. A couple of dogs watch as a flatbed wagon is loaded with ear corn, pulled by two very solid horses. Notice the blanket partially covering one of the horses.

Cradle and Scythe. Wheat is harveted on an Indiana farm with a cradle and scythe.

Above and Right. Mint is loaded and later pressed for its pungent and precious oil.

||||||||||||||||||||||||||||||||||||||||||||||||||||||||||||||||||||||||||||||||||

Threshing. A crew threshes Korean lespedeza, a legume that was introduced to the U.S. in 1919. The work is being done of the farm of Norton Garth, Treuton, Ky.

Lespedeza. Lespedeza is a drought-resistant, summer annual legume useful for pasture, hay and soil improvement.

Combining. One tractor pulls a McCormick-Deering combine while another pulls a grain drill.

Family Time. Everyone helps dig, grade and bag the potoatoes.

Corn Shucking. These farmers gathered in 1934 to shuck corn at a recently-widowed woman's farm.

Harvesting Potatoes. Homemade portable outfit, for grading and sacking potatoes on the farm of John Morsey in Antigo, Wis. This outfit could grade and sack about 1,200 bushels of potatoes a day.

Baling. Power pickup baler puts up alfalfa on farm of R.M. Jaimison in Garden City, Kan.

Threshing Soybeans. Two loaded wagons are pitched into the thresher on this farm in 1928.

Making Hay. Six mule teams mow hay.

Loaded. a wagonload of cabbage harvested from farm of A.H. Hahhoehsema, Muscatur, Iowa.

Teamwork. A farm wife drives the Allis-Chalmers tractor while her husband spreads the hay being stacked by the hayloader hidden behind the wagon.

Haymaking. Mowing and raking hay while a load of loose hay is ready to be unloaded at the gate leading to the farmyard.

Above. An early corn picker and tractor alongside a team of mules on a corn wagon.

Right. Baling straw brought by mules on bull rakes.

Combining. Wheat is harvested on the farm of George Deeman in Larned, Kan.

Straw Men. Baling straw left behind after combining.

Left. A sled corn cutter in 1931.

Above. Harvesting rice in Arkansas in 1933.

Above and Right. A team of horses on a buck rake push the alfalfa hay to men who load the hopper feeding the stationary haypress belt-powered by a tractor. The bales are then loaded on the truck. Near Chickasha, Okla., in 1932.

Threshing rice. Threshing rice with a Case outfit in El Campo, Texas.

Haying. A brand new Case baler is put to its first test on this Indiana farm.

IIIIIIIIIIIIIIIIIIIIIIIIIIIIIIIIIIIIIIIIIIIIIIIIIIIIIIIIII

Above. Loading hay onto a wagon pulled by four horses on the farm of Elmer Baughman, Long Grove, Iowa.

IIIIIIIIIIIIIIIIIIIIIIIIIIIIIIIIIIIIIIIIIIIIIIIIIIIIIIIIIIII

Right. Binding oats with three lovely gray Percherons.

||||||||||||||||||||||||||||||||||||||||||||||||||||||||||||||||||||||||||||

Left. Cutting oats on the farm of H.E. Thoeming, Blue Grass, Il.

Above. Another hay baling scene.

Left. An ox team in New Hampshire in 1915.

Above. Two-row corn-picker attachments quickly fill the wagons pulled behind.

Baling Straw. This shot shows the operation from another angle than many of the others. Notice the close attention the man is giving the wire-tying operation.

Ready for the Mow. A nice team of horses pull a loaded wagon by the hog pens on its way to the barn where the crop will be stored.

Hulling Clover Seed. Hulling clover seed with McCormick-Deering tractor and separator manufactured by Wood Brothers Thresher Company on the farm of J. Berlowitz, Tippecanoe County, Indiana.

Side delivery rake. Turning over a windrow.

America's Rural Yesterday

Chapter 5: General Fieldwork

Left and Above. Team of purebred Percheron mares on a rubber-tired spreader.

Above and Right. A nice team of mules bring a load of cow manure to the field to be spread.

Posing. Glenn Boram, son of Mr and Mrs. E.E. Boram near Noblesville, Ind., with his dog, Ted, and the farm horse, Tom, stop for their photo to be taken as they collect some potatoes for supper.

Big load. This is fitted with sideboards and two sets of beaters.

Spreading Limestone. Lloyd and Lyle Martin spreading limestone at the farm of Gilbert Powell near Lafayette, Ind.

Stepping out. This team appears to be walking quickly as it pulls a Moline LS200 spreader.

Broadcasting. Seeding oats with end gate seeder on the Ed Layden farm near West Point, Ind.

More broadcasting. Seeding oats with a team and an end gate seeder on the Stanley Normal Farm, Linden, Ind.

Above and Right. A trench is dug across a farm field using four mules prior to the laying of field tile.

Cotton Load. Two wagonloads of cotton begin their journey to the mill.